MICHAEL ROSE

A Miscellany for Flute

BOOK II

	piano	flute
Vilanelle (unaccompanied)		page 1
Ragtime	page 2	2
Burlesque	4	2
Pastorale (unaccompanied)		3
Canzona	6	4
Serenade (unaccompanied)		4
Nocturne	7	5
Caprice	10	6
Mazurka	12	6
Impromptu (unaccompanied)		7
Intermezzo	13	8

THE ASSOCIATED BOARD OF
THE ROYAL SCHOOLS OF MUSIC

for Sally

A MISCELLANY FOR FLUTE
BOOK II

MICHAEL ROSE

Ragtime

Fine

AB 2174

Dal Segno % al Fine

Burlesque

Canzona

Nocturne

Caprice

Mazurka

Intermezzo

for Sally

A MISCELLANY FOR FLUTE

BOOK II

MICHAEL ROSE

Vilanelle

(unaccompanied)

AB 2174

Ragtime

Tempo di Ragtime ♩ = 69

Burlesque

Allegretto molto giocoso ♩ = 118

Pastorale
(unaccompanied)

Canzona

Serenade
(unaccompanied)

Nocturne

Caprice

Mazurka

Impromptu
(unaccompanied)

Allegro scherzando ♩ = 120

8

Intermezzo